Thank you for purchasing the book. We hope you enjoy it
If you liked the book, please do not forget to support us
with a beautiful comment. Thank you!

D1501745

This coloring book is b

If found, please return to:

_____

_____

COLOR TEST :

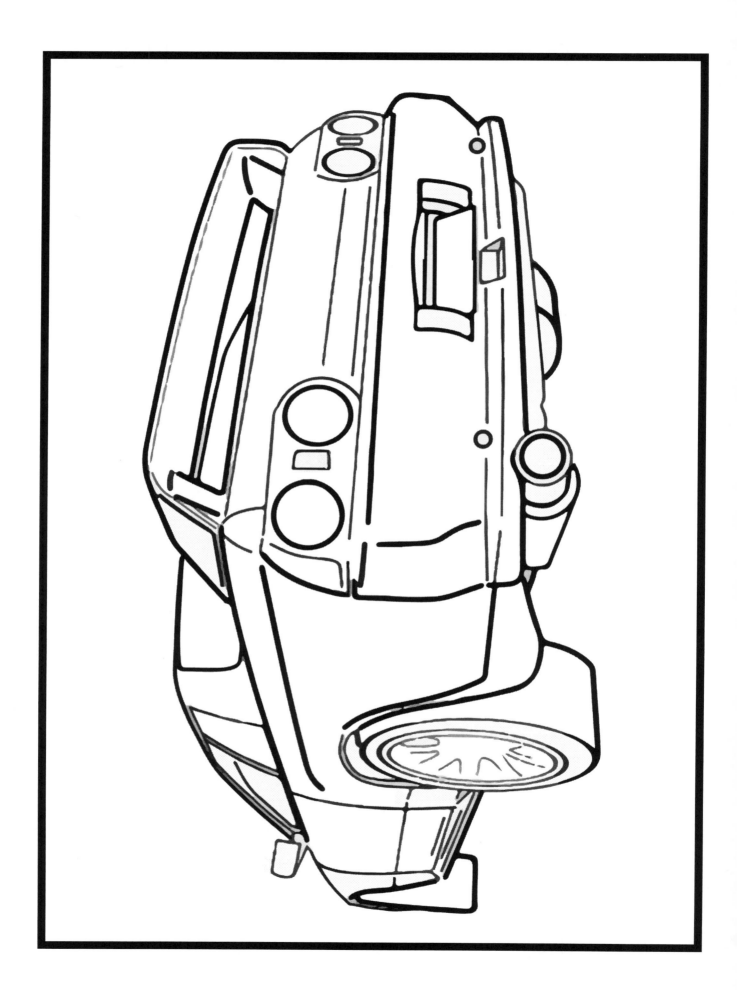

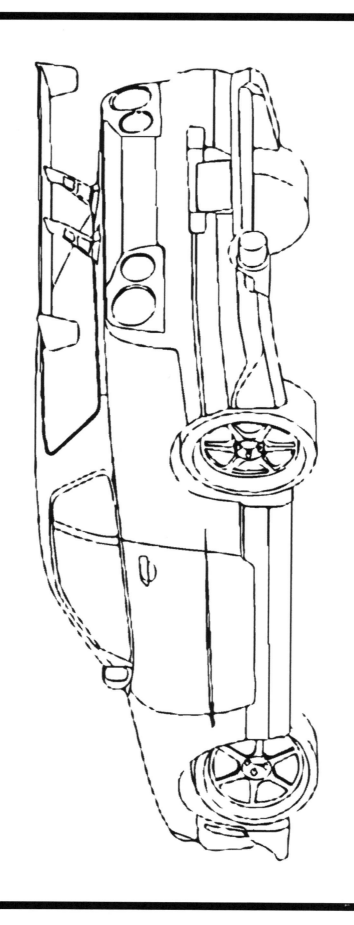

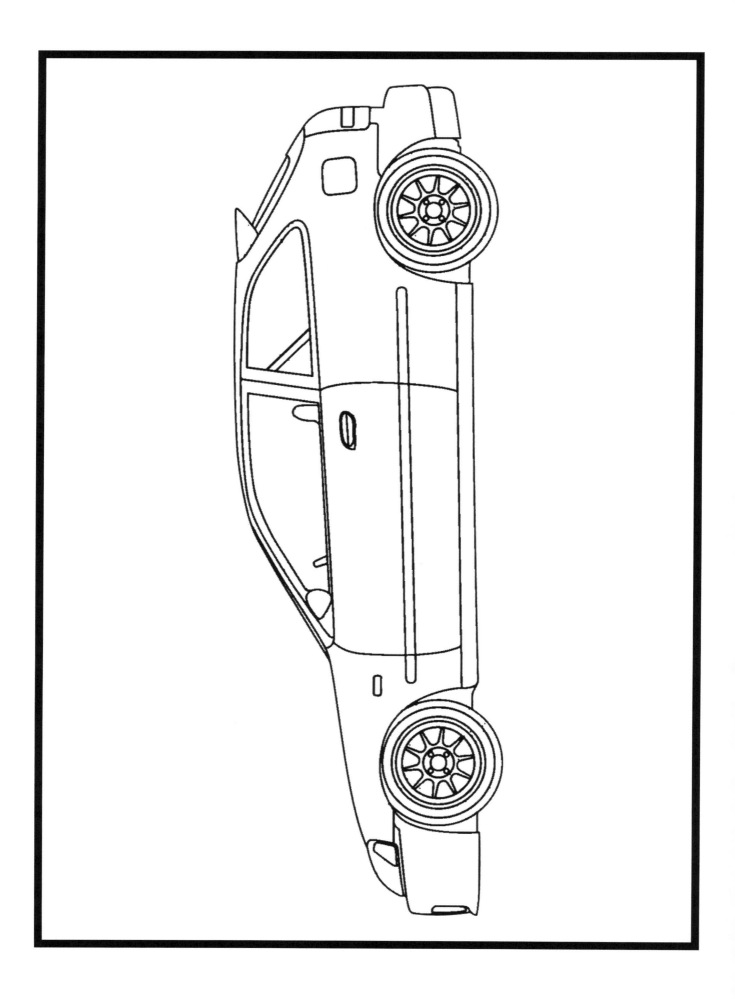

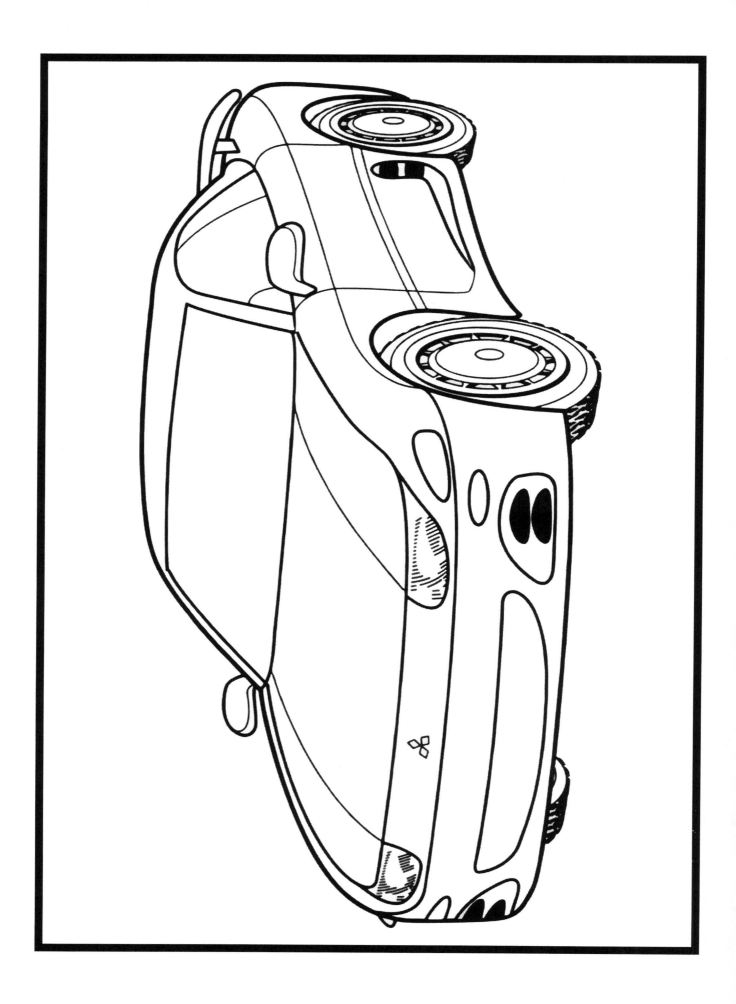

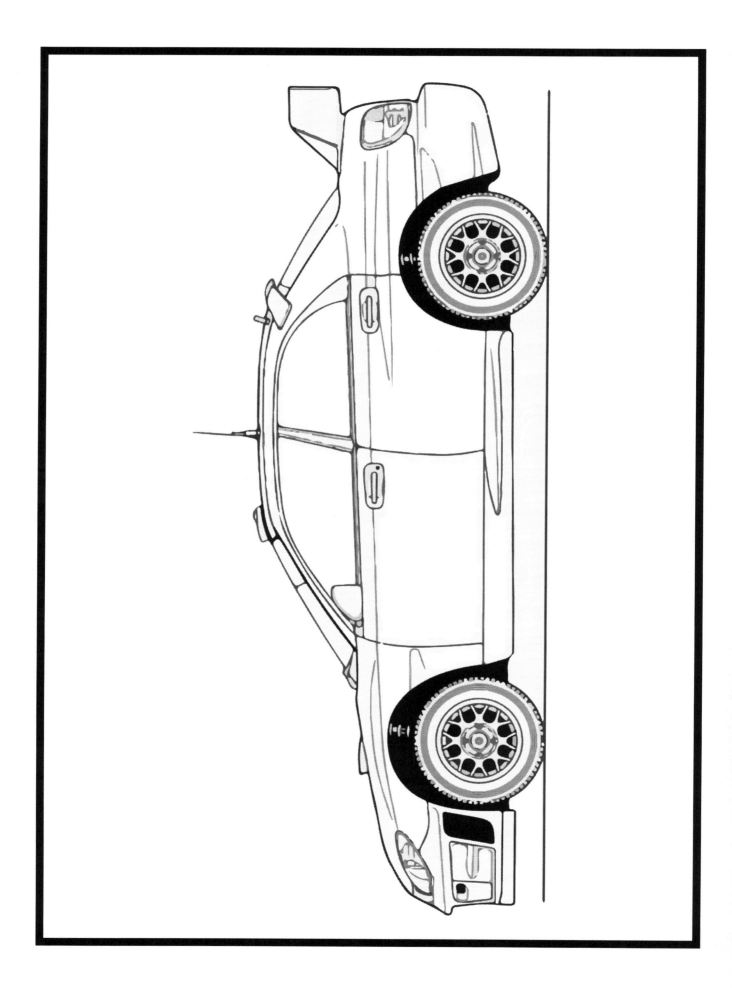

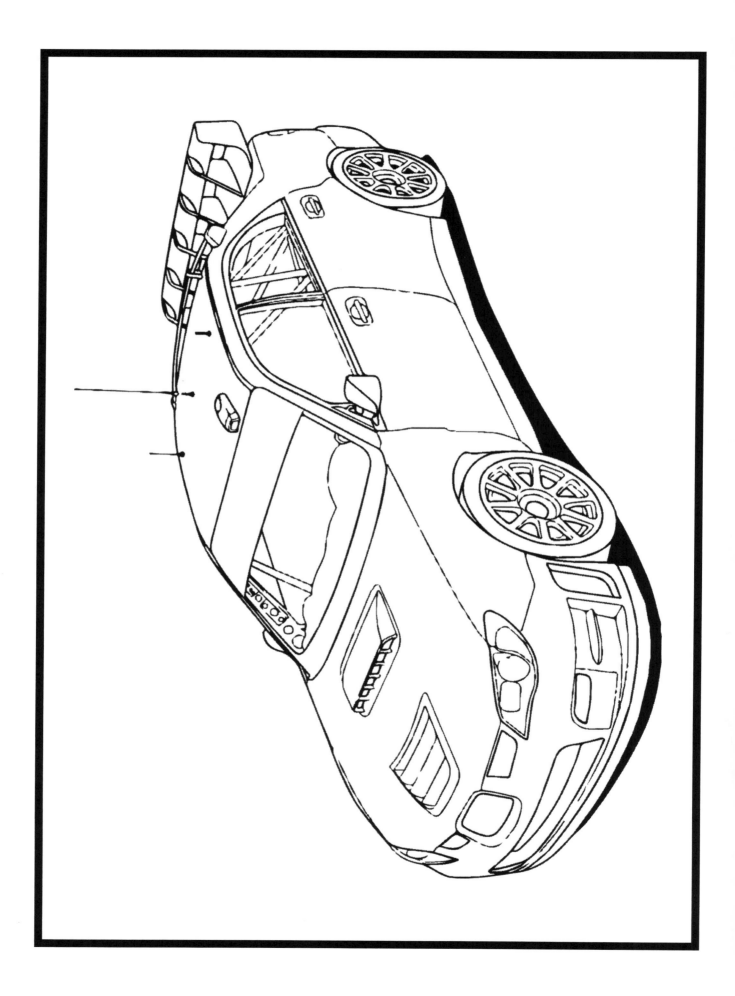

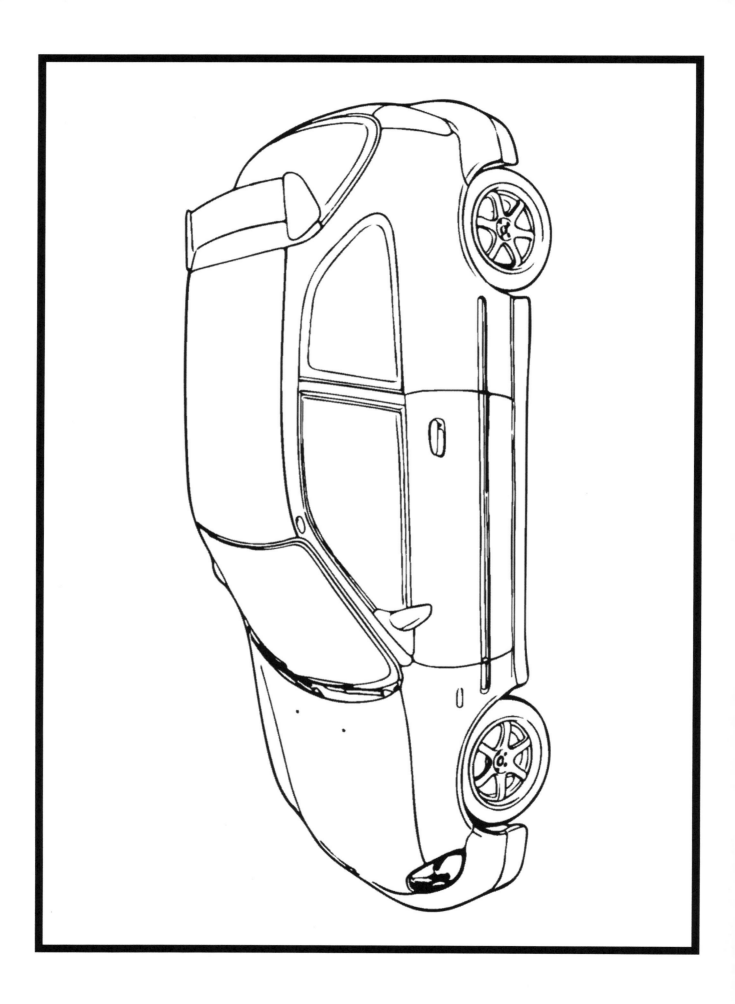

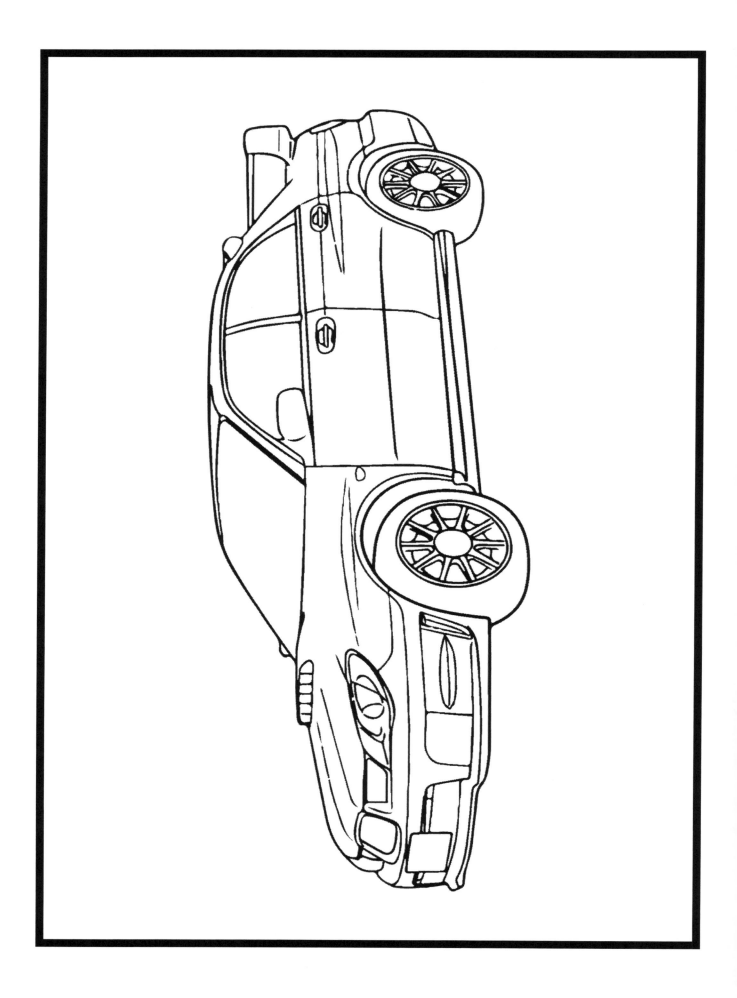

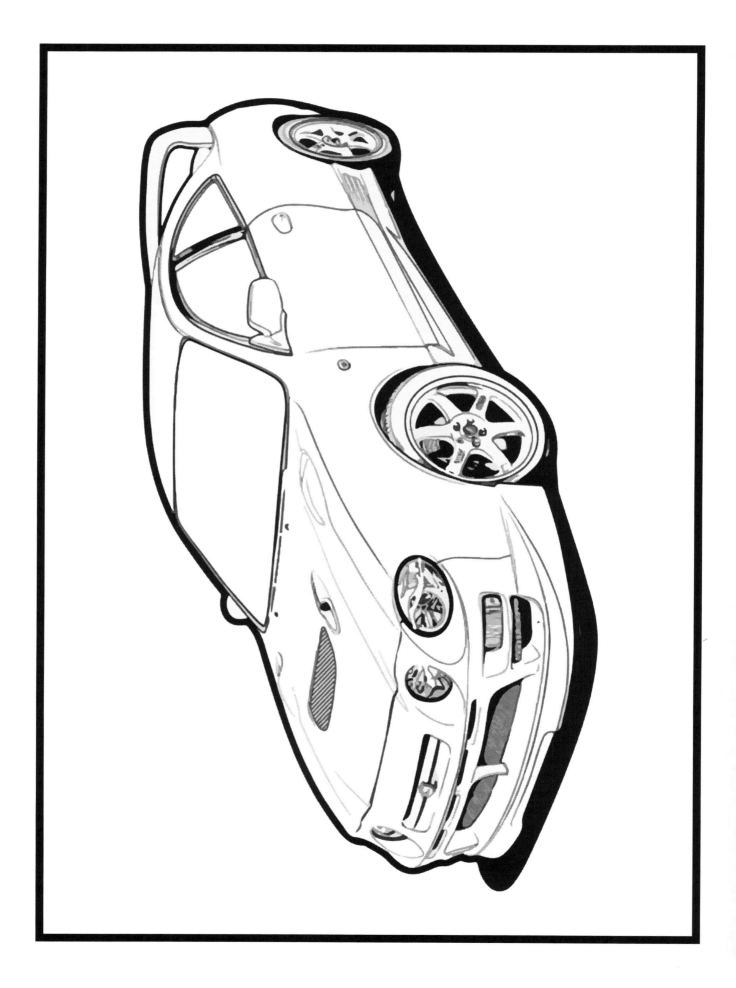

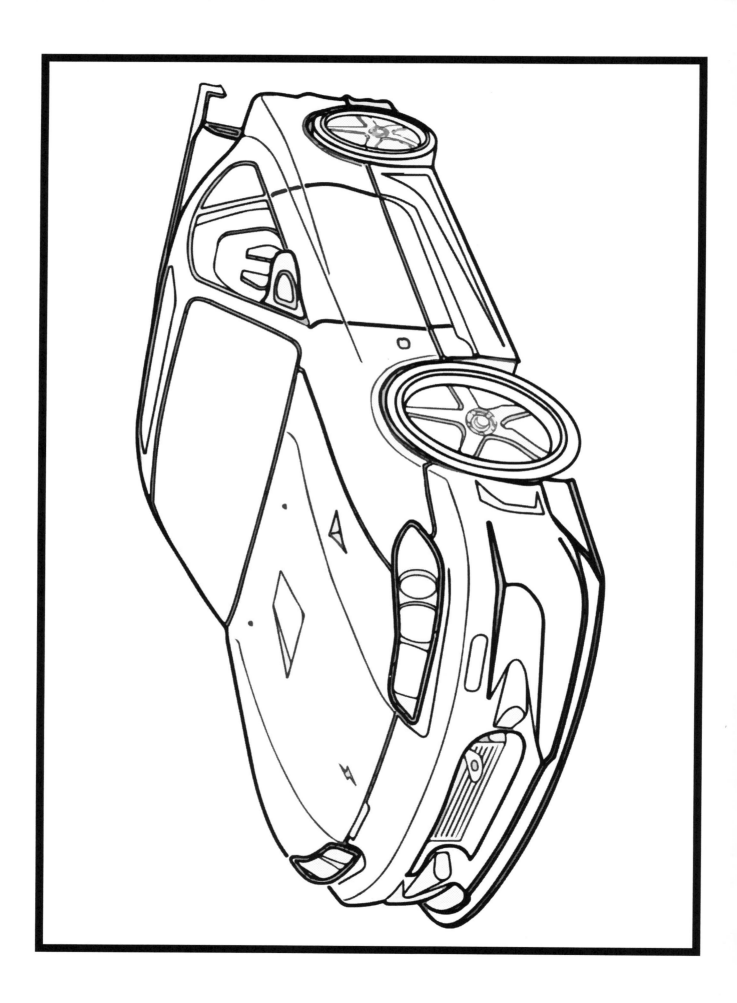

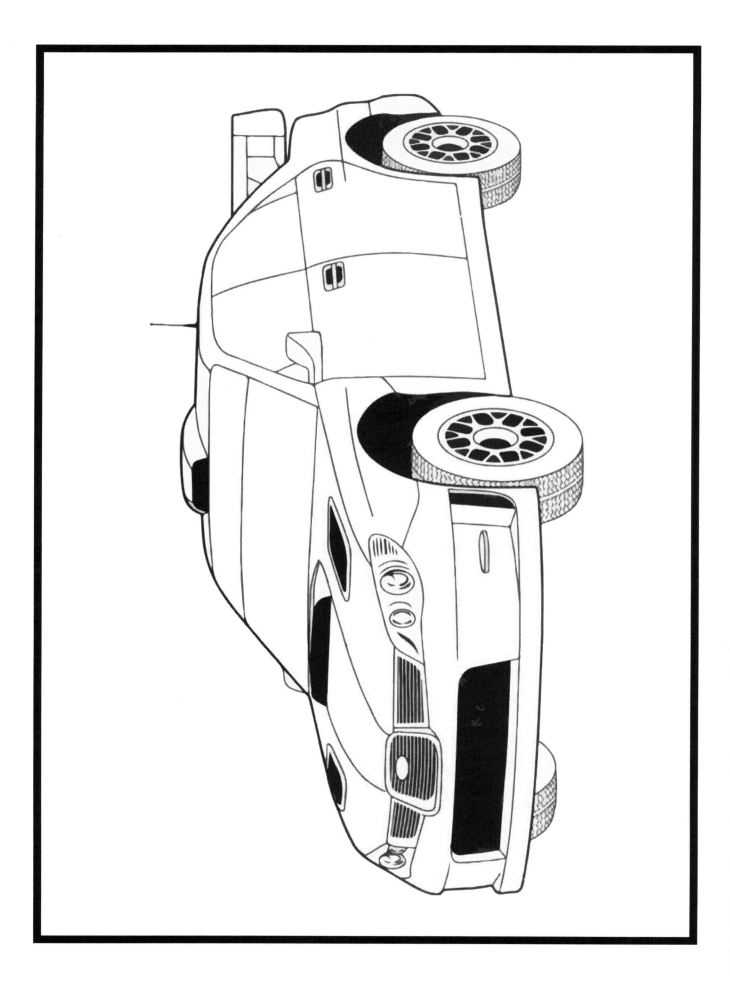

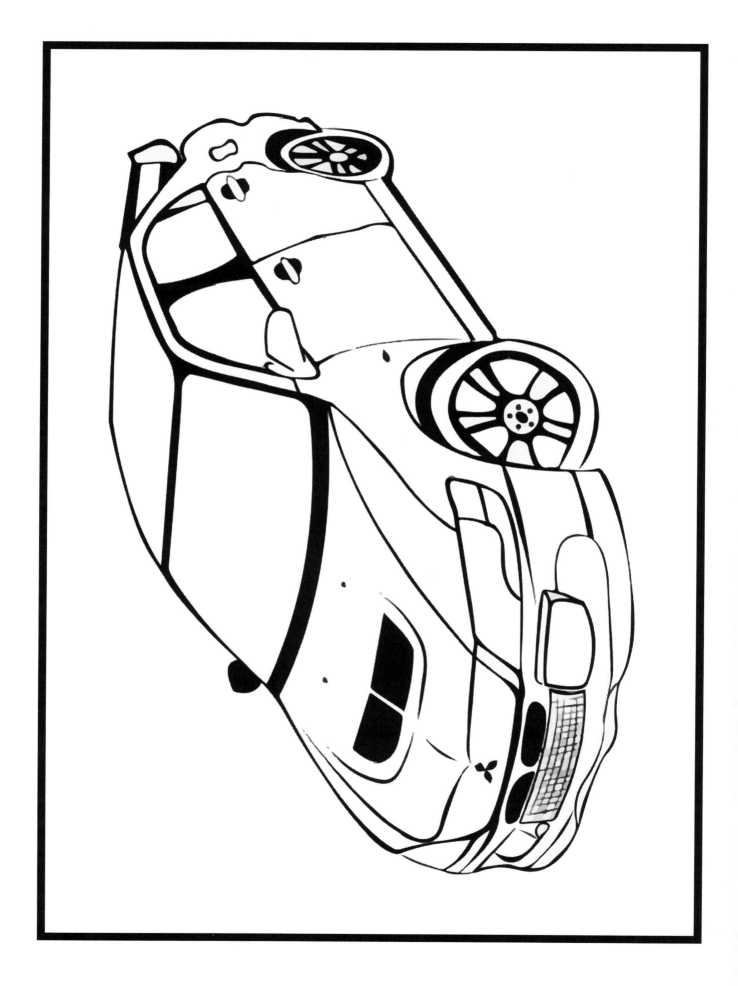

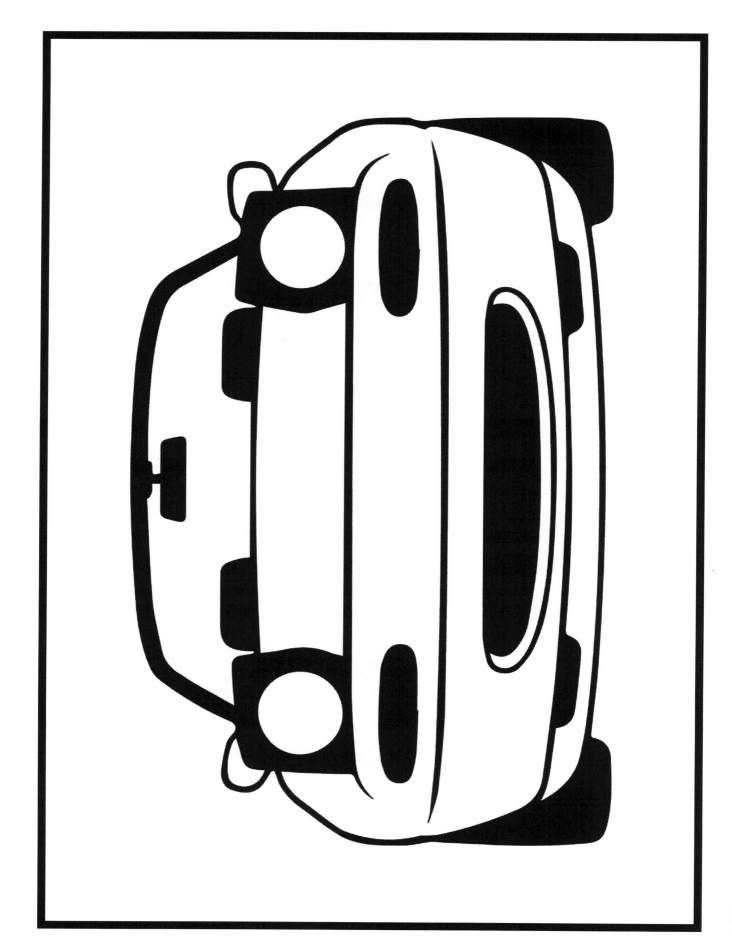

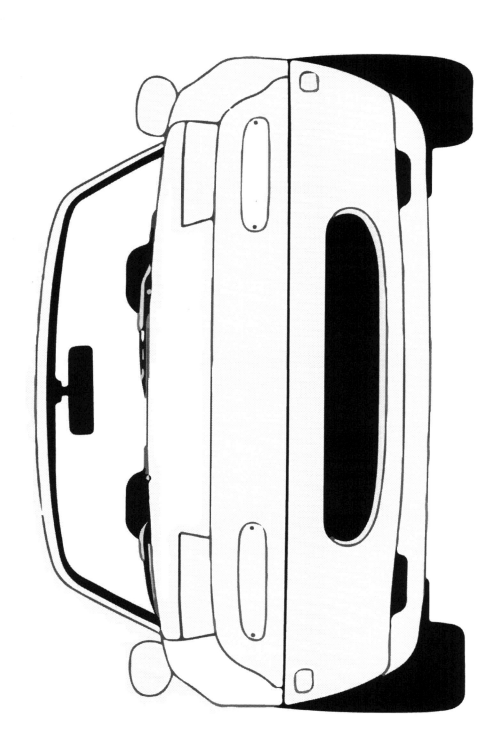

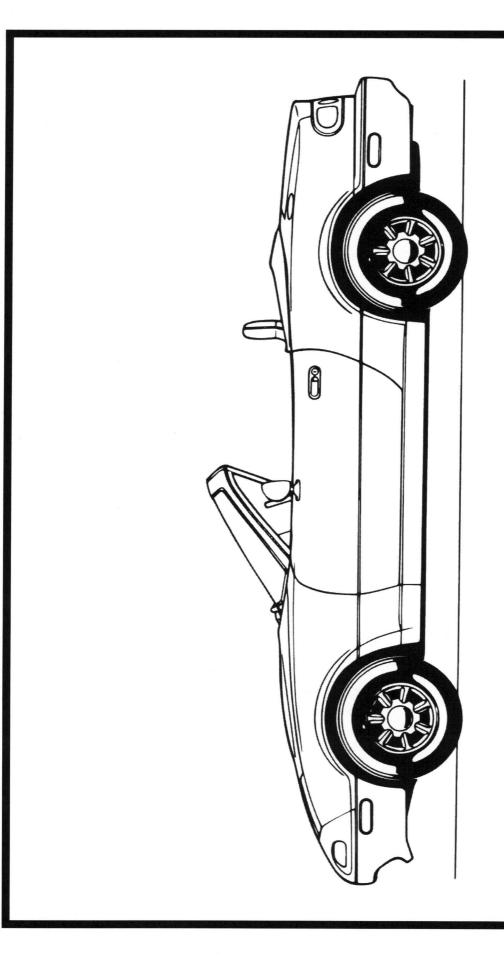

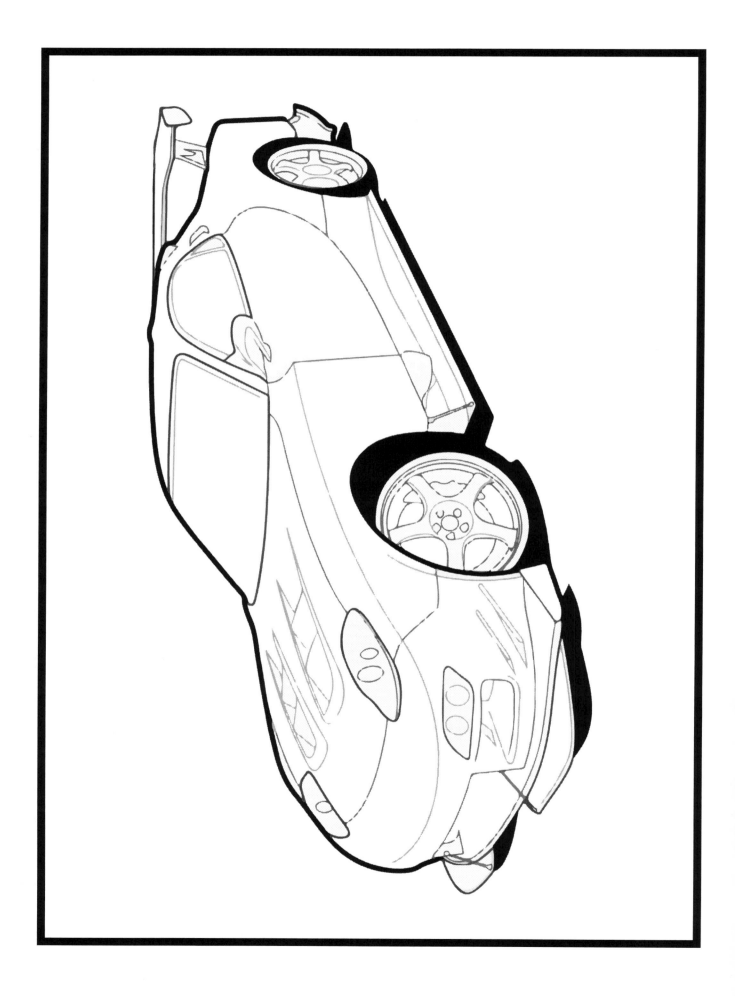

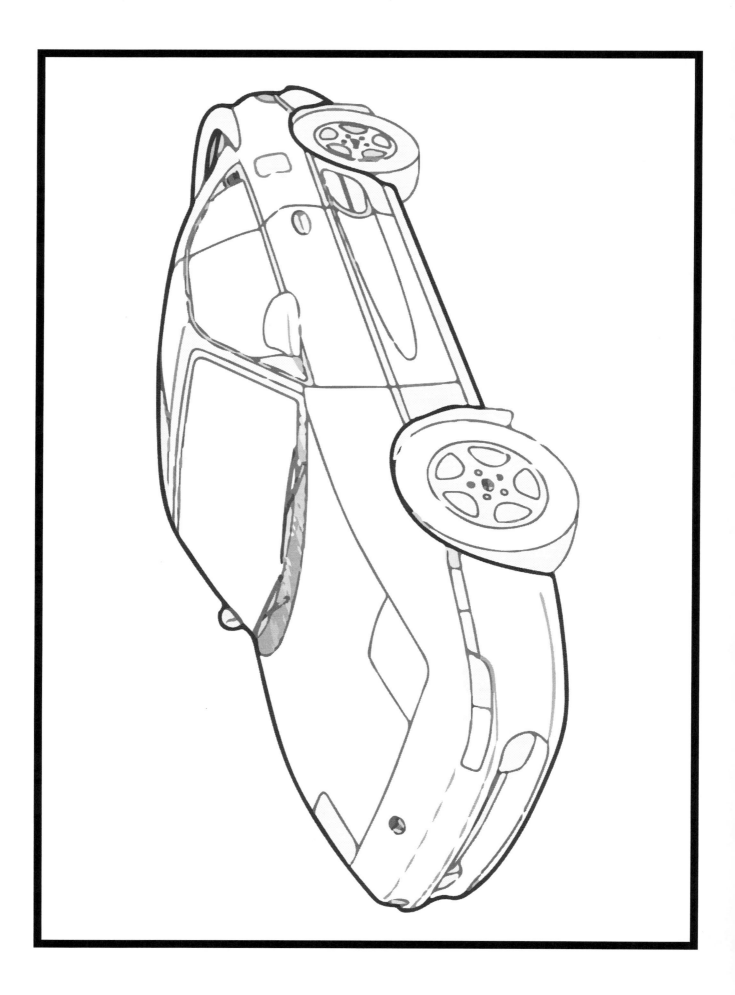

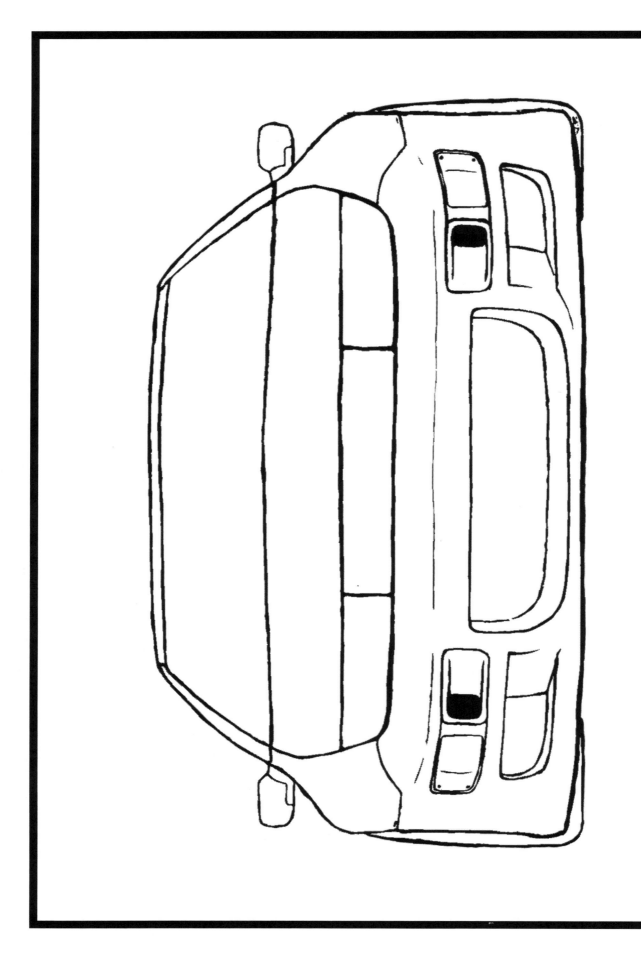

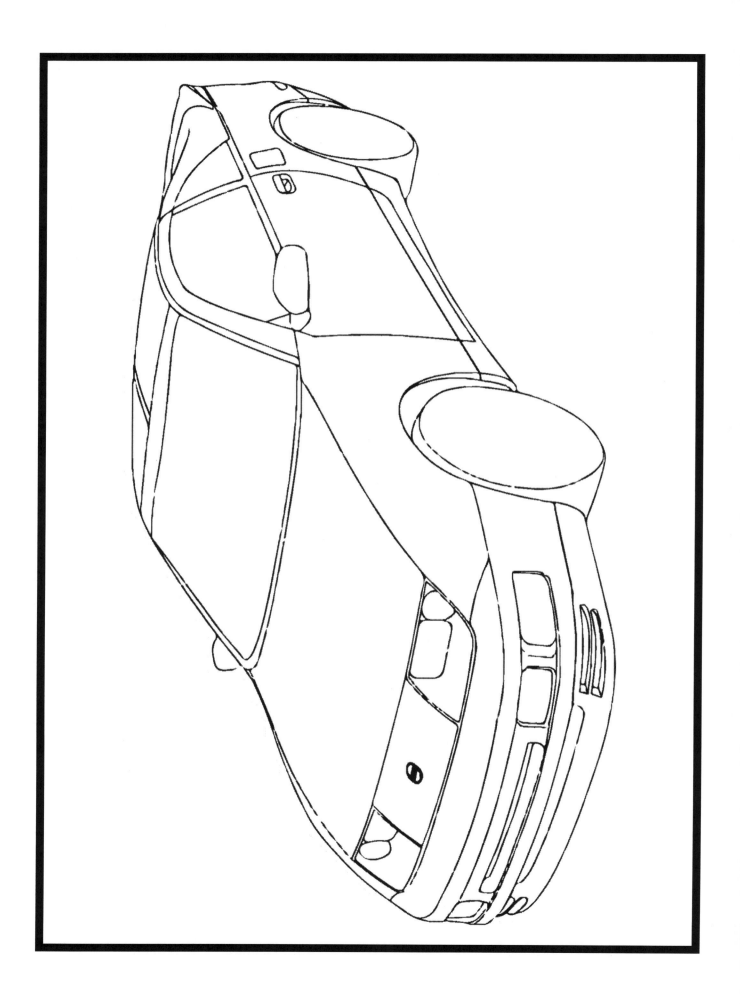

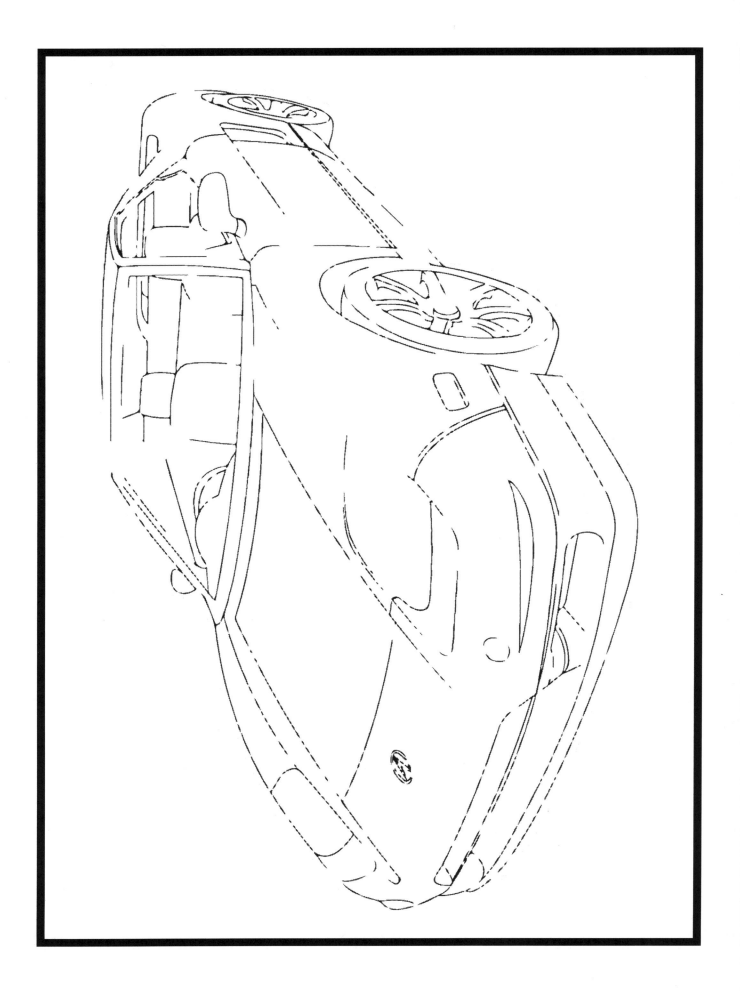

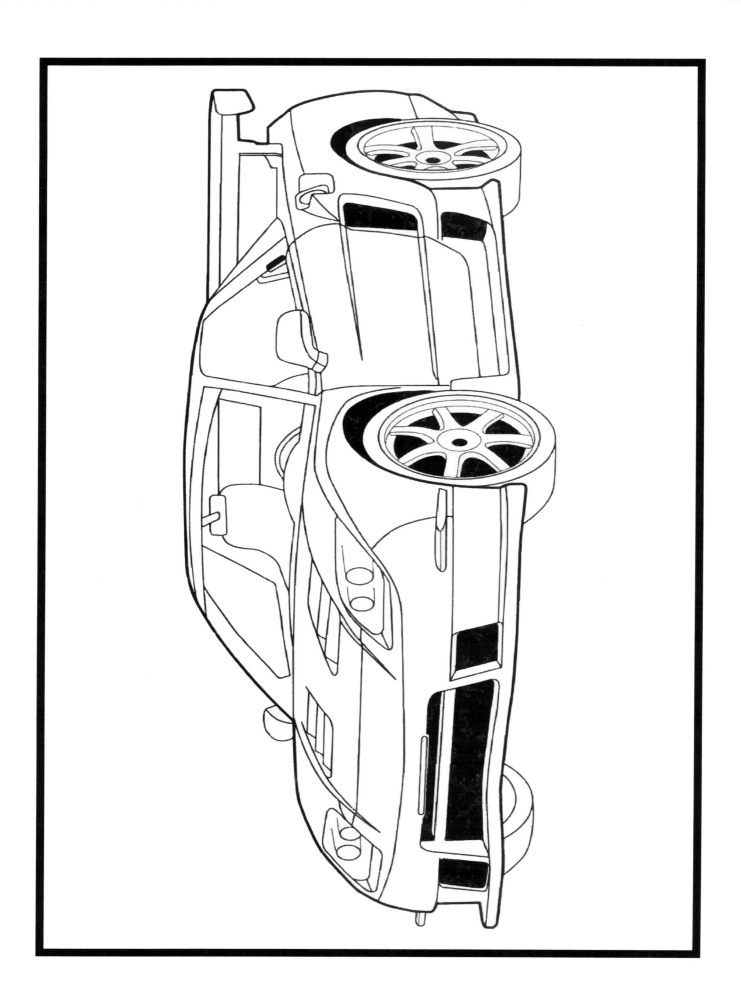

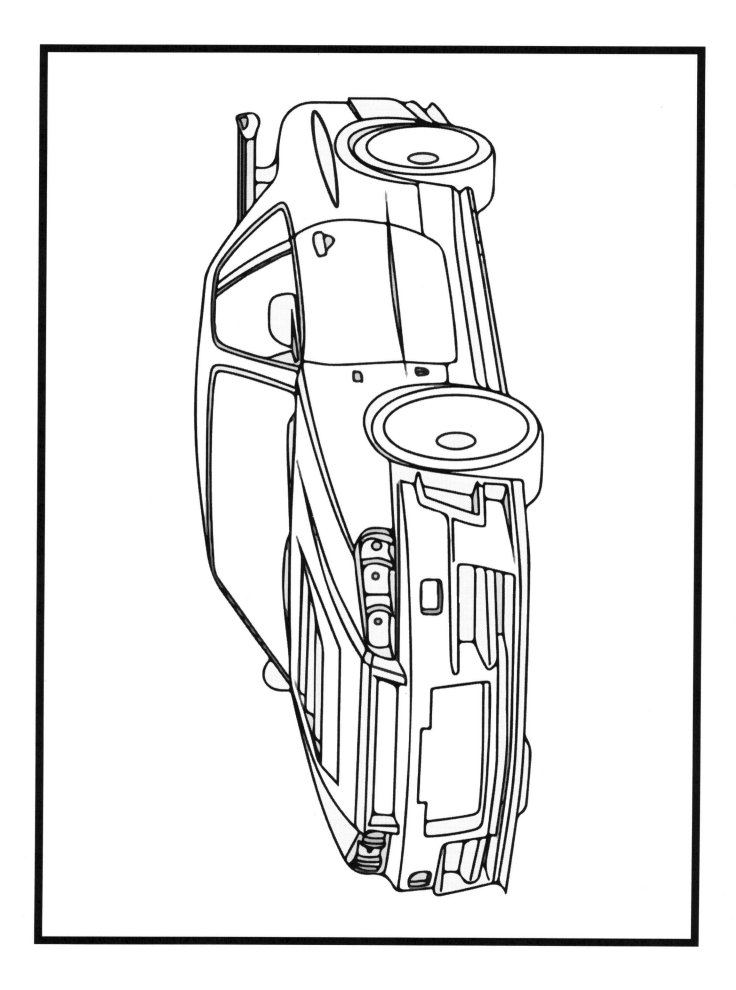

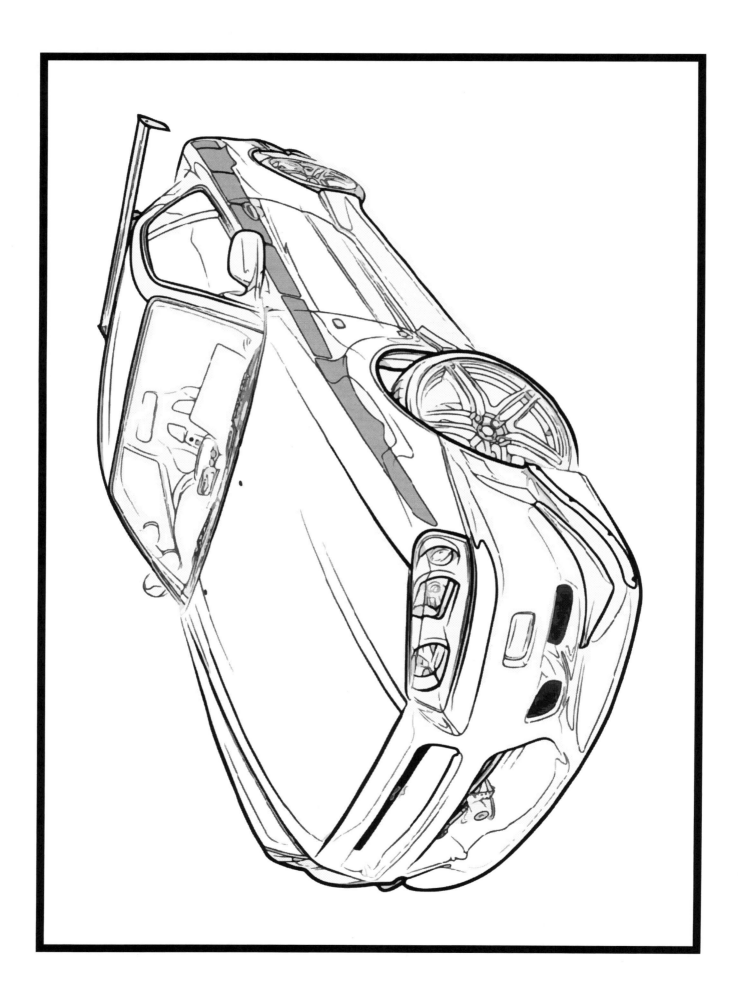

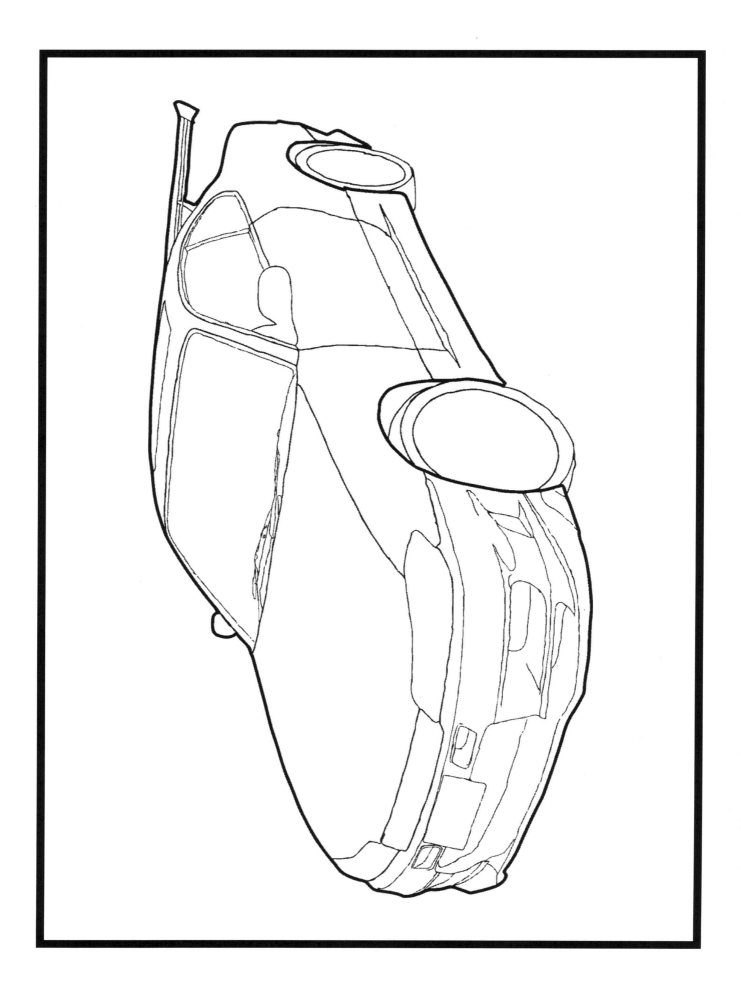

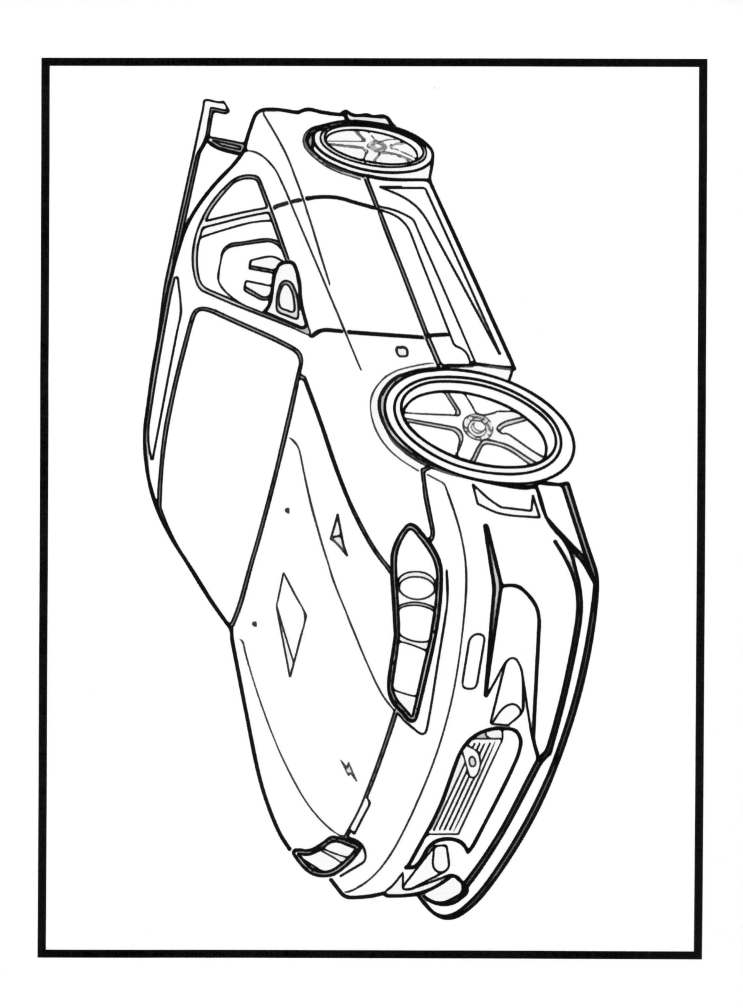

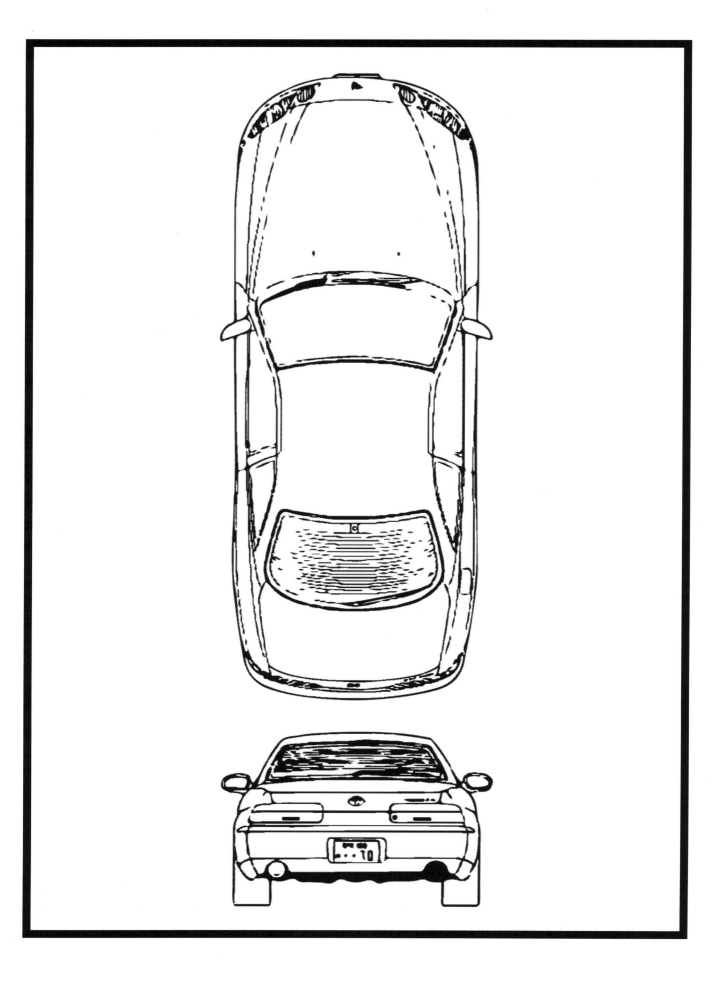

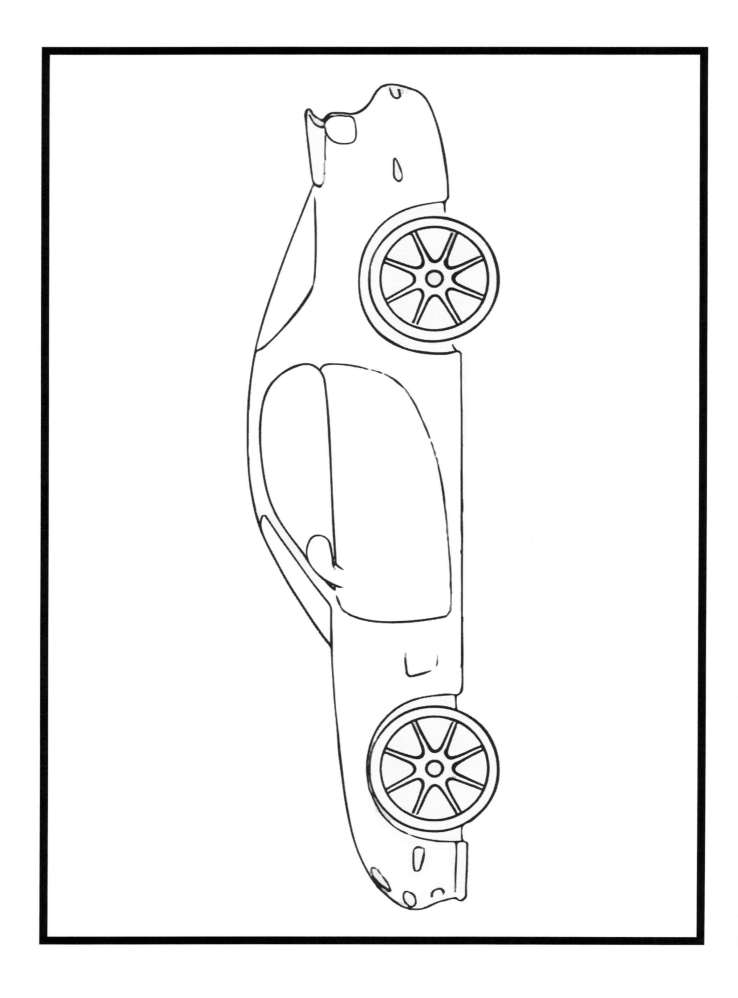

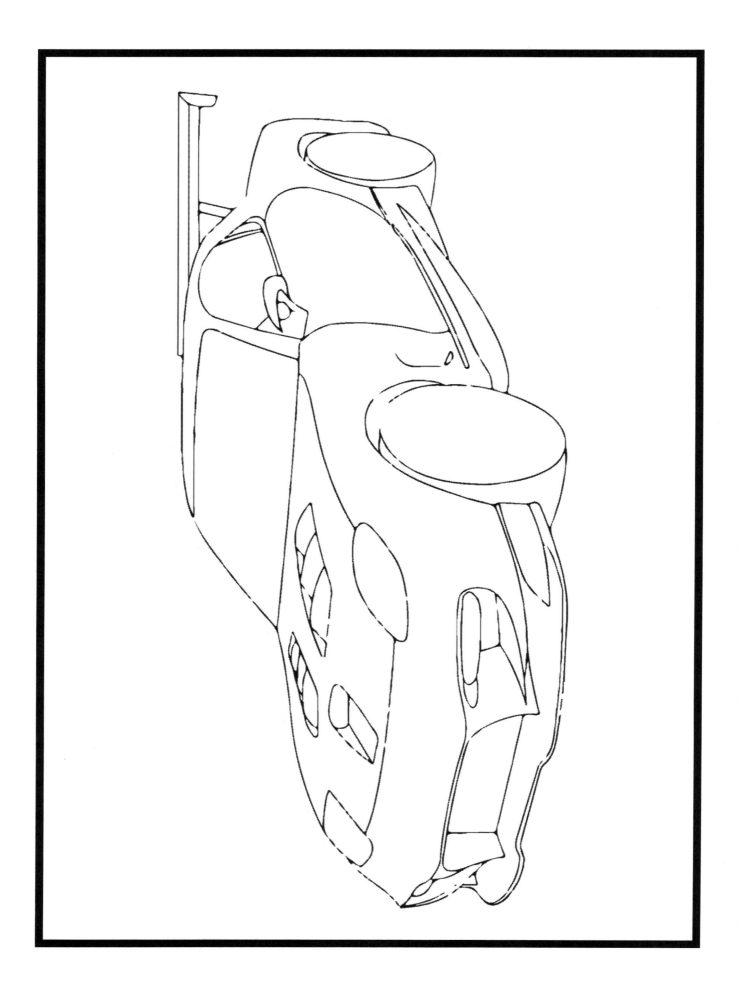

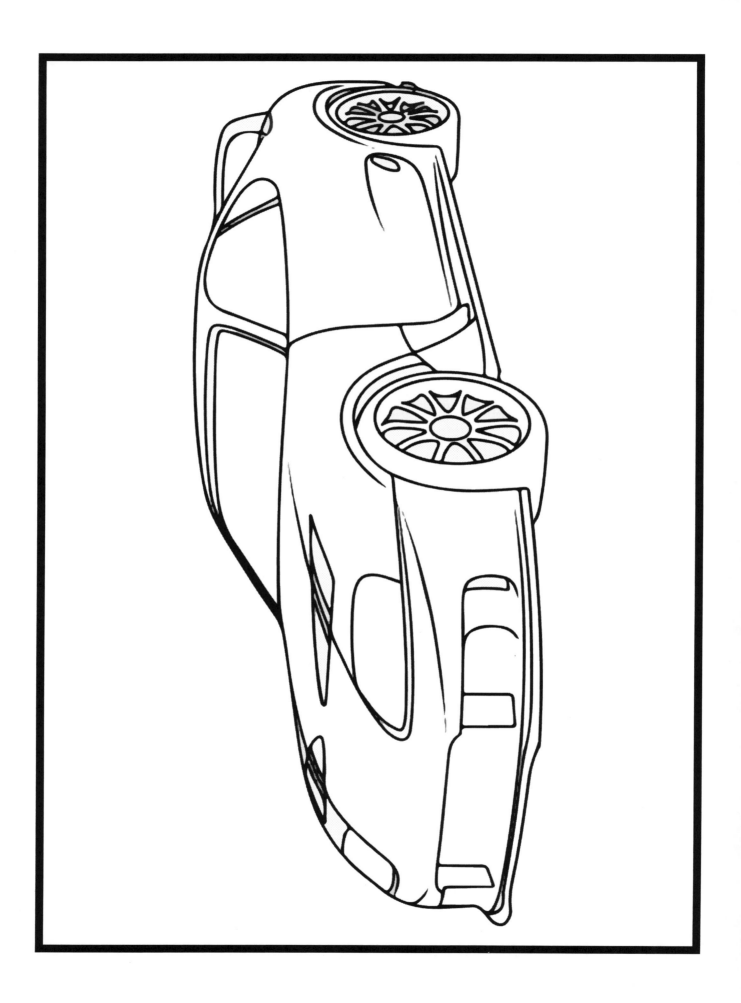

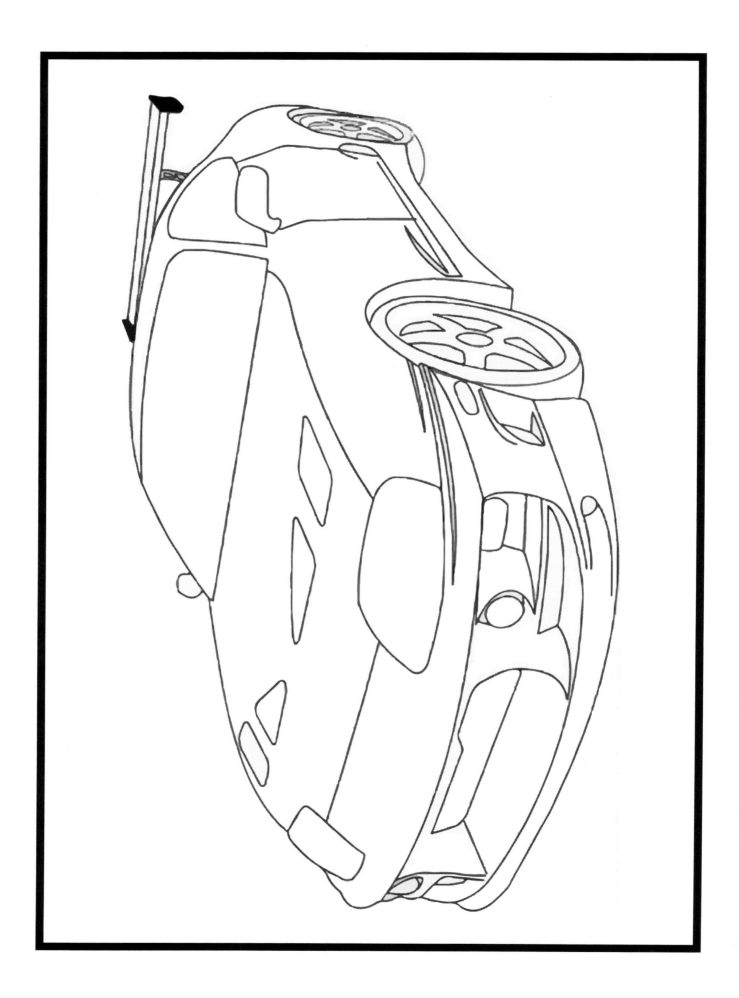

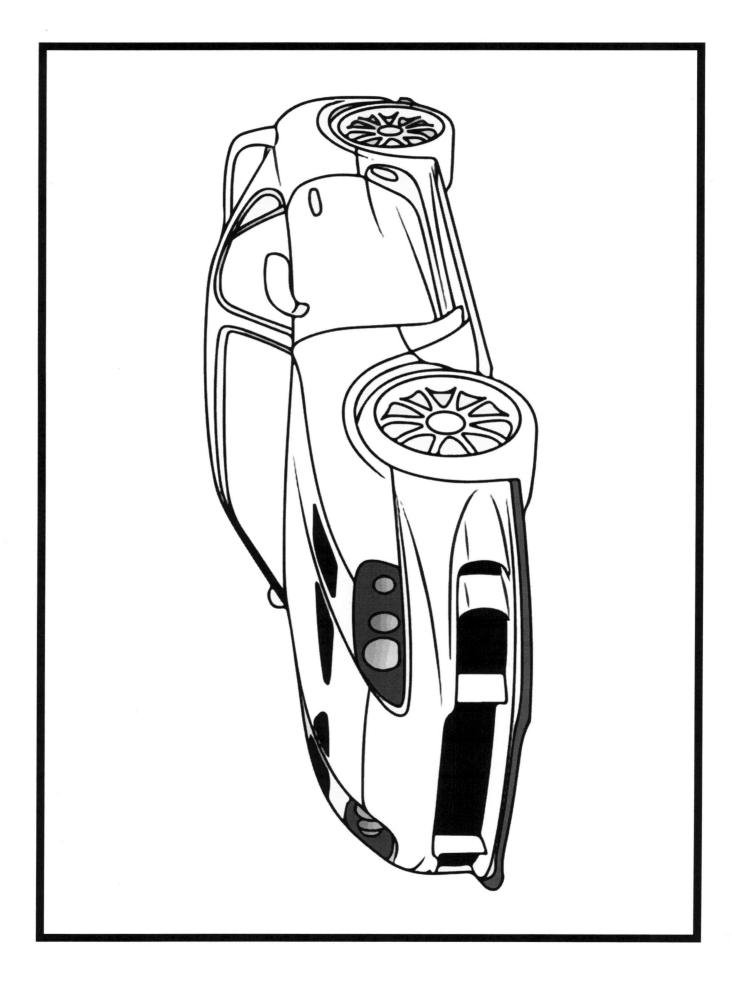

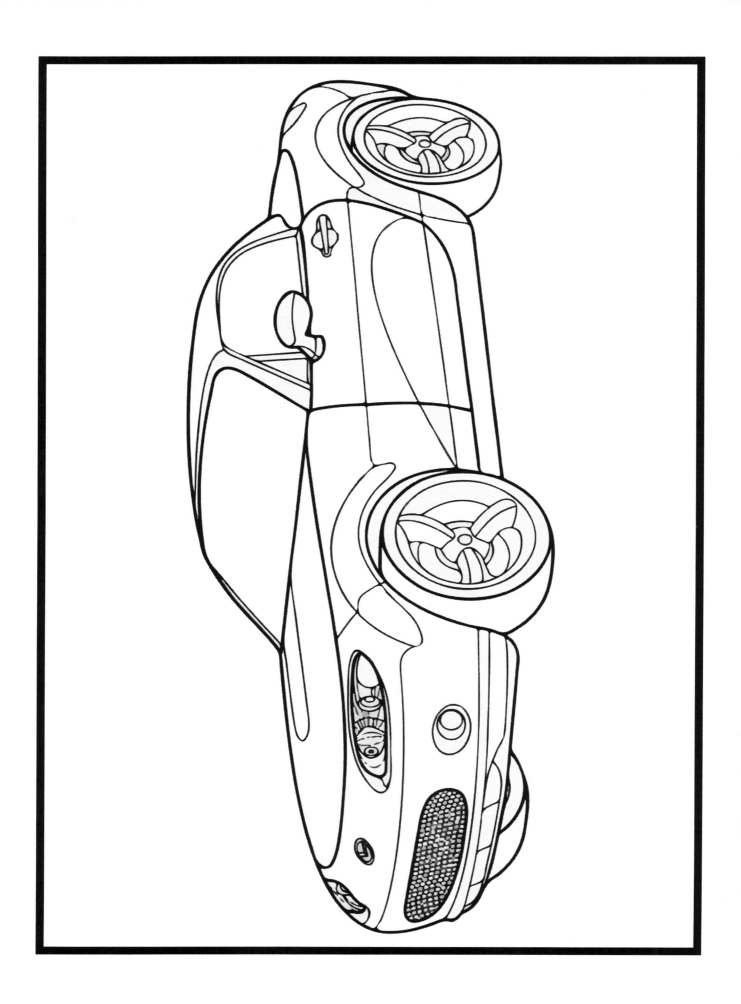

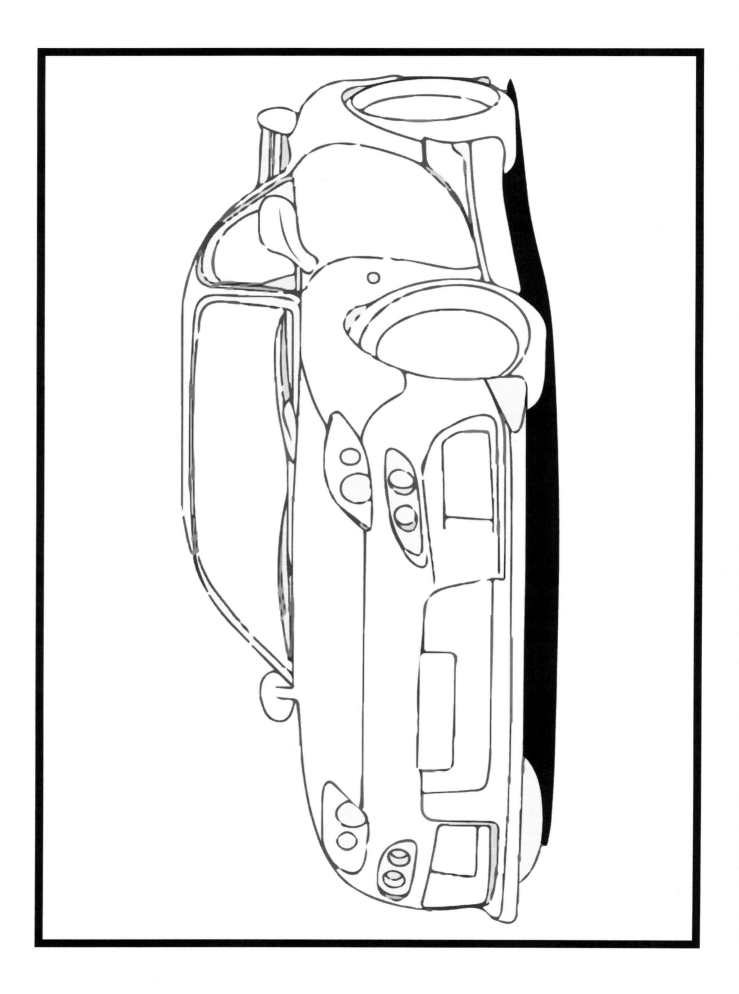

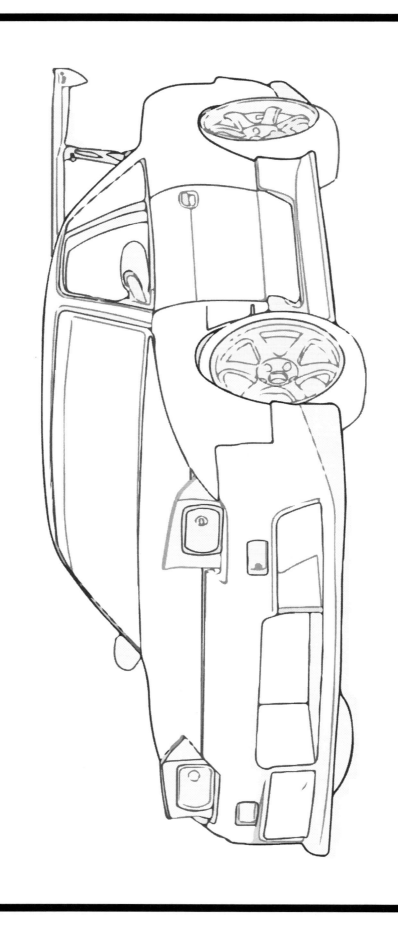

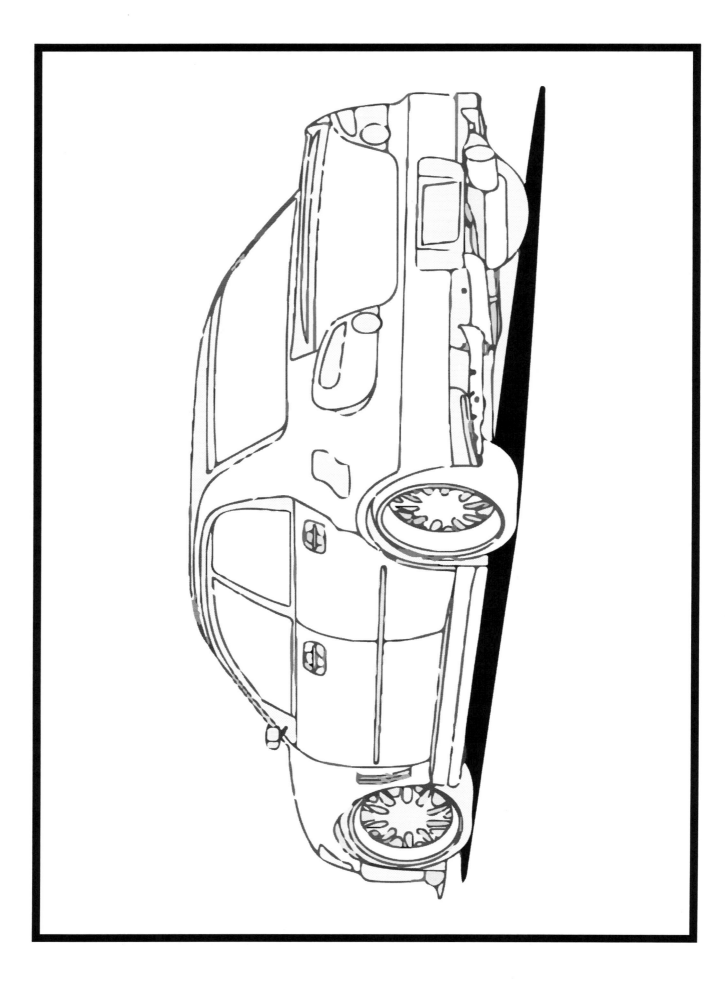

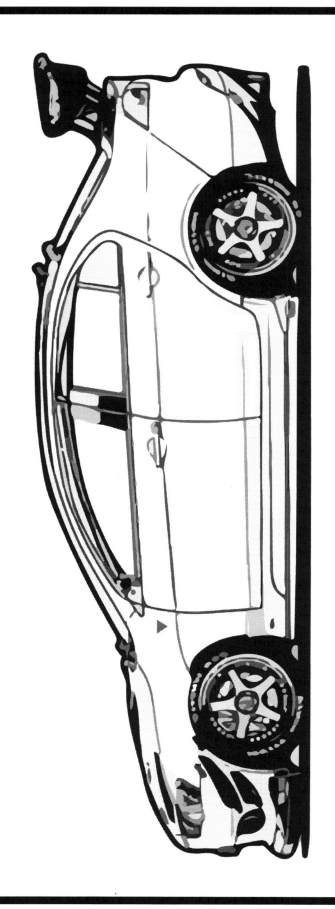

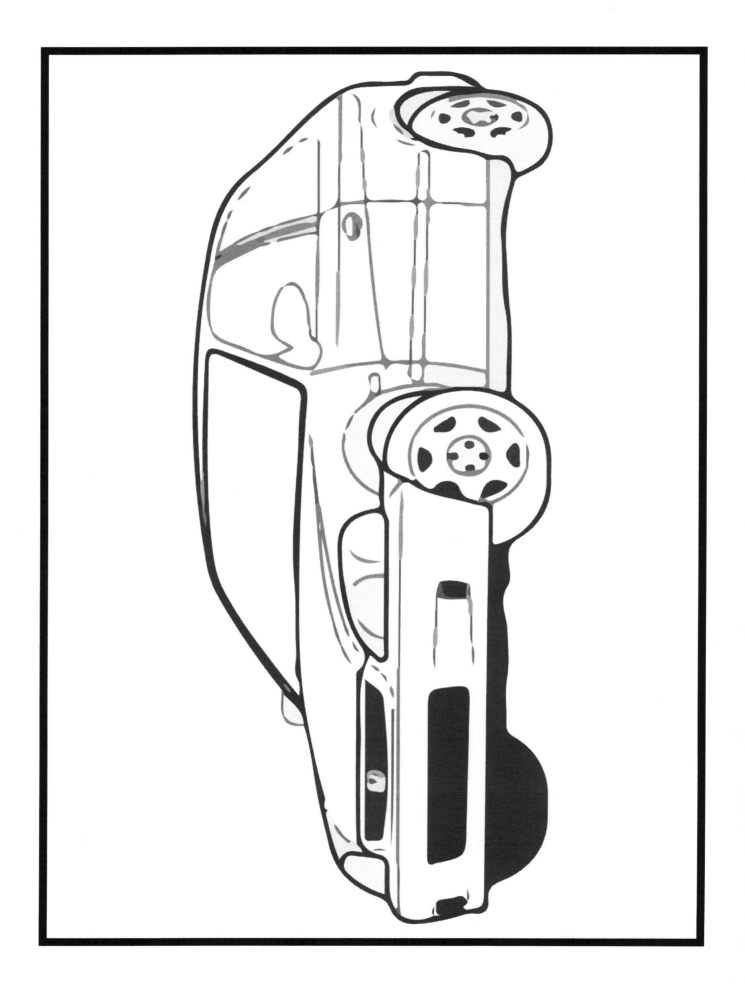

Made in the USA
Monee, IL
03 November 2022

17054429R00046